The Birthday Surprise

Pre-Reading
This alphabet story teaches all about letter names and sounds.

 "Gramps!" says Leap. "What shall we get? Mom's birthday's near!"
"Let's get a jet!"

GAME 1

GAME 2

CAP
BAT
JET
PIG
MOP
RUG

GO

Alligator Baking Cookies

"I've just the spot to help you pick.

GAME 1

GAME 2

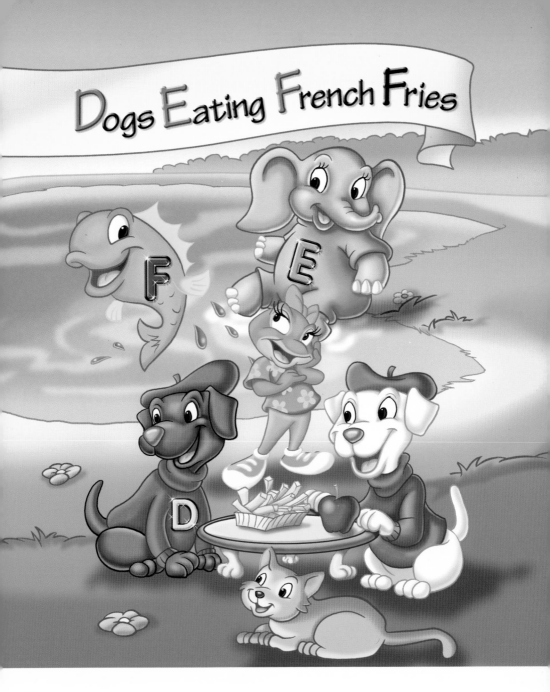

Dogs Eating French Fries

The Alphabet Pond," says Gramps. "Go, quick!"

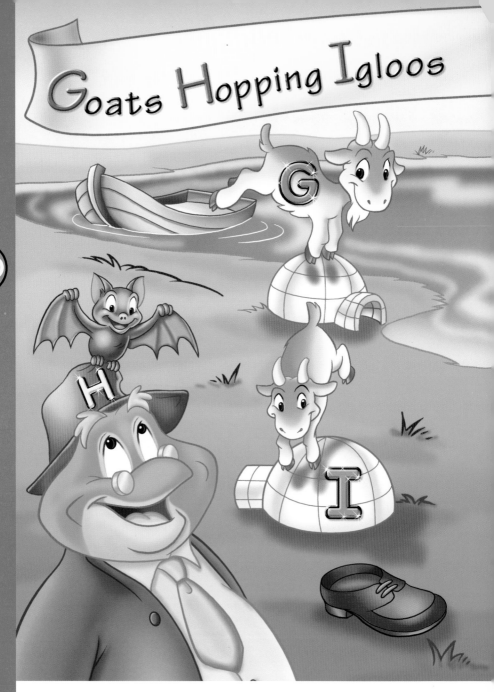

Goats Hopping Igloos

GO

"A lamp, a kite,
a wind-up car.

STOP

GAME 1

GAME 2

Jumping Kittens Laughing

The perfect gift cannot be far."

GO

STOP

 Lil spies some eggs.
Leap sees an otter.

GAME 1

GAME 2

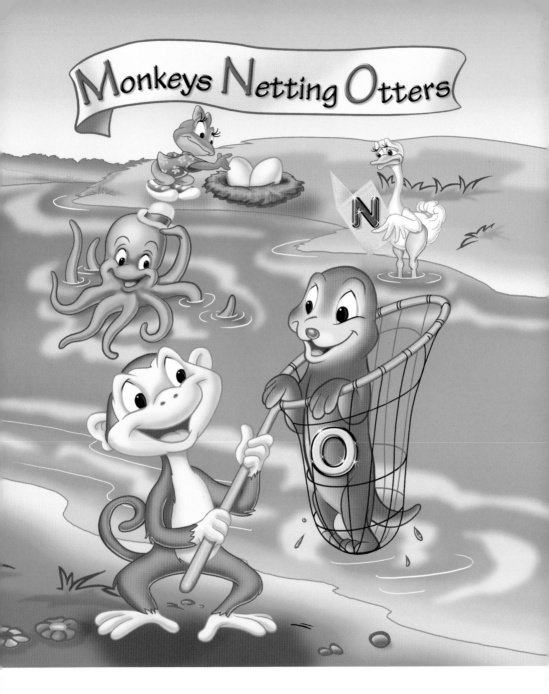

Monkeys Netting Otters

Tad thinks his search is getting hotter!

Panda Queen Relaxing

GO

STOP

Lil's sad. She knows they don't have long.

GAME 1

GAME 2

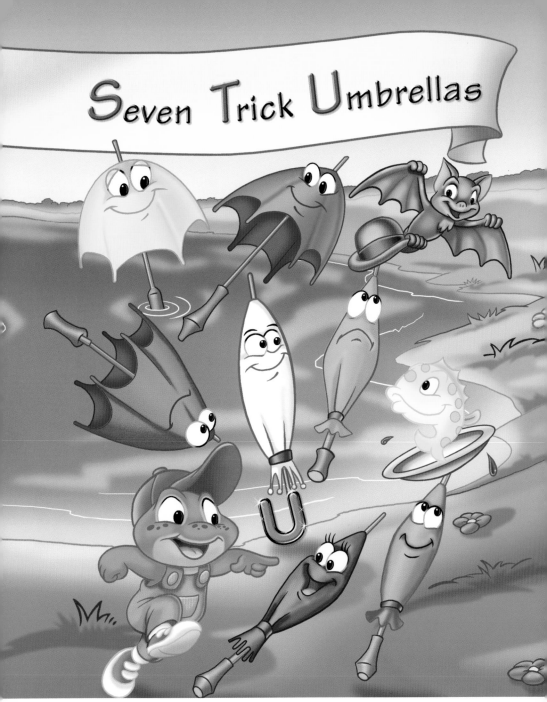

Seven Trick Umbrellas

 Then...Tad sings
an umbrella song!

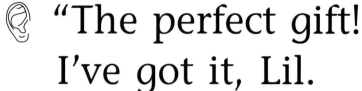
"The perfect gift! I've got it, Lil.

GAME 1

GAME 2

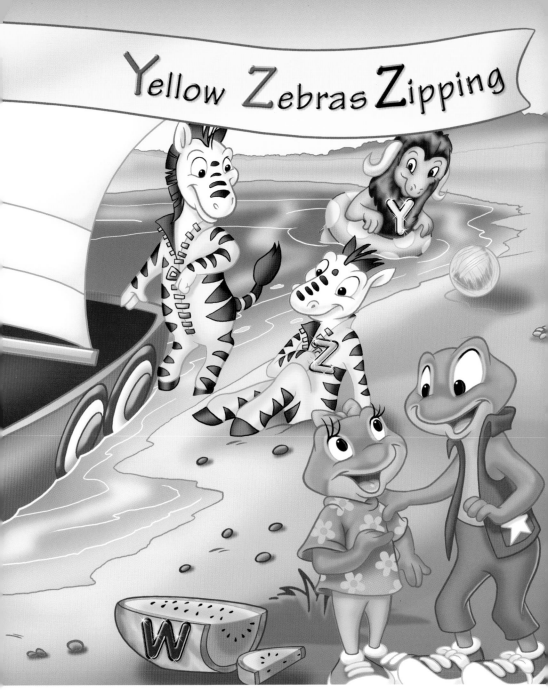

Yellow Zebras Zipping

 And Mom will love it!"
"Yes! She will!"

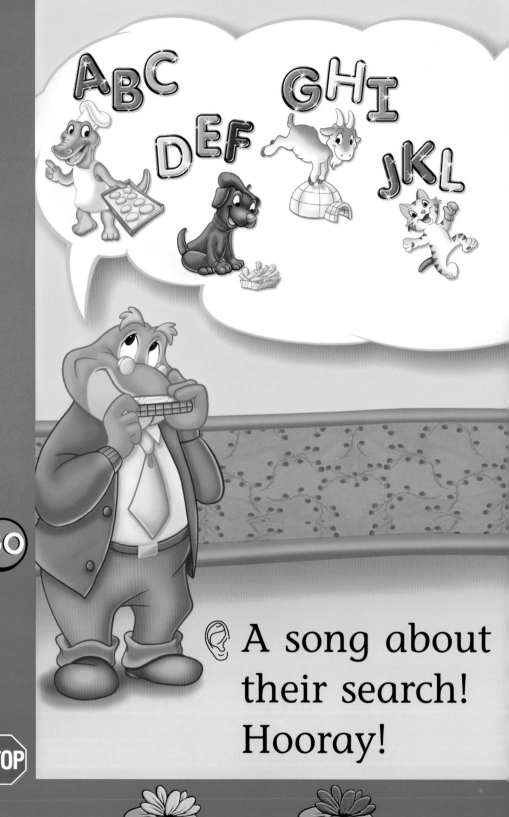

A song about their search! Hooray!

GAME 1

GAME 2

 A red rose too,
for Mom's great day.

 D
 E
 F

 J
 K
 L

 P
 Q
 R

 V
 W
 X

Welcome to the LeapPad® Library!

LeapFrog® LEAP•START
Preschool-K • Up to Age 5

LEAP•START Books:
Reading Readiness and Simple Activities

 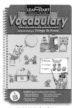  

© 1991 Richard Scarry

LeapFrog® LEAP•1
Preschool-Grade 1 • Ages 4-6

LEAP•1 Books:
Learning to Read and Introduction to Simple Subjects

© 1999 Disney Enterprises, Inc.   © 1999 Hanna-Barbera

LeapFrog® LEAP•2
Grades 1-3 • Ages 6-8

LEAP•2 Books:
Reading Practice and School-Related Subjects

™ & © 1998 Hanna-Barbera   © 1998 Marc Brown   ™ & © 2001 DC Comics

LeapFrog® LEAP•3
Grades 3-5 • Ages 8-10

LEAP•3 Books:
Reading Comprehension and Reading to Learn

 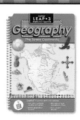  

**There are loads of books to choose from in the complete *LeapPad* library.
Go to: www.leapfrog.com to pick your favorite one!**